The Song of
Marian Anderson

Mc Graw Hill **SRA**

Columbus, OH

SRAonline.com

 SRA

Send all inquiries to this address:
SRA/McGraw-Hill
4400 Easton Commons
Columbus, OH 43219

ISBN: 978-0-07-608863-8
MHID: 0-07-608863-4

1 2 3 4 5 6 7 8 9 NOR 13 12 11 10 09 08 07

"Grams, where's that old jazz record you used to play for us?" Natasha asked her great-grandmother. Natasha and her brother Ricky were at their great-grandmother's house for the afternoon. They always enjoyed the trip because she loved music just as much as they did. She collected every type of music there was.

"Why, I'm sure it's up in the attic with every other one. Come on, let's go find it," Grams said, getting to her feet.

Natasha and Ricky could not believe how many records their great-grandmother had. Piles, stacks, and boxes filled the entire attic, yet Grams always knew exactly where each record was.

Natasha and Ricky waited as Grams looked through her boxes.

Natasha squealed with delight as her great-grandmother pulled out the old jazz record. "You found it!" she cried, taking the record over to the record player and starting it up.

"As a toddler you absolutely loved the third song," Grams said. She began tapping her feet to the music. "You loved to dance to it." Ricky continued to flip through the records from the box that Grams had brought over. It had everything from blues to country. Natasha grabbed a record as Ricky flipped past it.

"This album cover is beautiful!" Natasha gushed. "Marian Anderson? I've never heard of her."

Grams gasped. "You children don't know Marian Anderson? Why, you're surely missing out. Put this record on when the other one finishes," Grams instructed. Natasha replaced the record with Marian Anderson's, and a rich voice flooded through the speakers.

"She's pretty impressive," Ricky said over the music.

"Her voice is amazing!" Natasha exclaimed.

Grams closed her eyes as she listened to the music. "She always did have a beautiful voice with a rich tone and a marvelous range. She could sing anything, but she became important for something besides her voice."

"What did she do?" Ricky asked.

Grams smiled and pulled out several more Marian Anderson records. "Marian Anderson displayed great talent at a very young age, but her family was poor and could not afford voice lessons. She began singing at her local church, where she could perform every part."

Ricky's and Natasha's mouths dropped open in surprise. "She was so good that a voice teacher gave her free lessons for a year! She won the first prize in a contest with three hundred competitors, and she was wonderful." Grams stopped and sighed. "Sadly, not everyone wanted to hear her sing."

Natasha and Ricky were confused. "Why wouldn't people want to hear her sing?" Ricky asked.

Grams frowned. "Marian Anderson lived from 1897 to 1993. She became popular in the 1930s, and that time was a difficult time for blacks in America. Some white people did not like blacks just because their skin was dark."

"That's not very fair," Natasha interjected. "That's like me not liking Ricky because he's wearing a red shirt. It's all so superficial."

Grams nodded. "You are wise beyond your years, Natasha. Most people, of all colors, see things that way. But some powerful people in Marian Anderson's time still felt skin color was an issue."

"Her singing career started growing. In 1939 she tried
to rent a concert hall in Washington, D.C., but she was
refused because of her skin color."

"That's not fair!" Ricky cried.

Grams nodded. "I know, and many people in Marian's
time knew it too. It became a great controversy, and
many people protested the group that owned the hall.
Many people, both black and white, knew that it was
wrong. They formed a committee to get recital space for
Marian. Eleanor Roosevelt, the First Lady at the time,
resigned from the group that refused to host Marian."

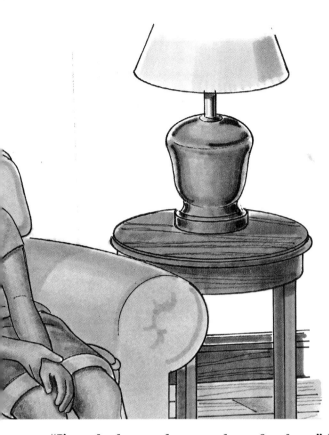

"I'm glad people stood up for her," Natasha said.

"Me too, child!" Grams exclaimed, laughing. "She deserved it, and when the first lady started talking about it, suddenly it became headline news. Marian was offered the Lincoln Memorial as a stage. I was in Washington, D.C., visiting an old friend, and we jumped at the chance to hear Marian sing."

"You mean you actually got to hear Marian Anderson sing live?" Ricky asked with disbelief.

"Oh, yes, and it was amazing! We joined more than seventy-five thousand other people to hear Marian Anderson sing."

"That's a lot of people," Natasha said with awe.

"That's nothing, because millions more people listened to Marian sing over the radio," Grams explained. "We were among people of every race, waiting for Ms. Marian Anderson to grace us with her songs. She was full of dignity as she stood in front of Abraham Lincoln's statue. It was an amazing experience I'll never forget."

"I'm glad she got to sing," Ricky said.

"Me too," Grams said. "She helped to destroy barriers based on race. The transformation to acceptance did not happen overnight. She and many others worked hard for it, though."

Grams pointed to the piles of albums that Ricky had stacked. "Marian inspired many artists and entertainers. She refused to be judged by the color of her skin. Sometimes people still turned her away. She continued to open doors for blacks."

"Good for her!" Natasha exclaimed. "I'm glad she fought them."

"Many people realized that when Marian was able to alert them to the injustice. The day Marian sang at the Lincoln Memorial was an important day for everybody. It set the wheels of justice in motion," Grams added.

"Marian Anderson even inspired my friend and me to stand up to racial barriers," Grams said.

"What did you do?" Ricky asked excitedly.

Grams got an old book and returned to the couch. Inside clippings of Marian Anderson dotted the pages along with pictures of young children. "Who are those people?" Natasha asked.

"That is my friend and me. These children are students we tutored. We taught them about their heritage and how important it was. We taught them to treat everyone equally, regardless of skin color. It was a real triumph to see those children grow to accept everyone."

"Grams, that's really terrific," Natasha said.

"I'm proud that you did something," Ricky added.

"Oh, I did lots of things. We wrote letters to the government, asking them to change laws that were unfair to blacks. We peacefully protested places that refused blacks."

"You're really incredible, Grams," Natasha said proudly.

Grams laughed humbly. "I just felt like it was my duty. Marian's art influenced me, and I wanted future artists to be able to affect more people without the fight that Marian had. Artists like the two of you. You both are very talented musicians and will have an impact wherever you perform."

"Thank you, Grams," Natasha said.

Grams hugged her and Ricky and then looked at her watch and said, "Speaking of talented musicians, you two need to get moving! Your music lessons begin in half an hour."

The three rose and began cleaning up the records. "Grams? Could we take one or two of these Marian Anderson records home with us to listen to on Mom and Dad's record player?" Ricky asked.

Grams nodded. "Yes, of course, and next time you come over we can listen to more of her records. I have several somewhere in all these piles."

"I had a great time, Grams," Natasha said. "Thank you."

"Anytime," Grams said smiling. "I'm glad Marian Anderson interested you children. She made an impact that will last for generations."

"Maybe one day we could make an impact with our own music," Ricky said, pausing, "but the barrier has already been broken down, I guess."

"There are still many injustices on this planet. People will always need helping," Grams said.

Ricky and Natasha agreed that they would touch others with their art just as Marian Anderson had, and they headed to their music lessons wondering whom they could help first.

Vocabulary

jazz (jaz) (page 3) *n.* Music that has strong rhythm and accented notes that fall in unexpected places.

blues (blo͞oz) (page 5) *n.* Music that sounds sad and has a jazz rhythm.

controversy (kon´ trə vûr´ sē) (page 8) *n.* A disagreement; dispute.

dignity (dig´ ni tē) (page 10) *n.* The condition of showing one's pride and worthiness in a confident manner.

transformation (trans´ form ā´ shən) (page 10) *n.* The act or instance of transforming; a marked change.

alert (ə lûrt´) (page 11) *adj.* Watching carefully; attentive.

heritage (her´ i tij) (page 12) *n.* Something handed down from earlier generations or from the past; tradition.

triumph (trī´ umf) (page 12) *n.* A great success.

Comprehension Focus:
Making Inferences

1. What inferences can you make about what kind of person Marian Anderson was?

2. What inferences can you make about the kind of people Ricky and Natasha will grow up to be?